FUN to LEARN
Scienc

G000123814

Graham Peacock
Illustrated by Ian Newsham

Educational Advisory Panel

Bernard Ashley – Head teacher and author

Diana Bentley – Language adviser

Peter Patilla – Lecturer and author

Susie Sainsbury – Nursery teacher

WALKER BOOKS
AND SUBSIDIARIES
LONDON • BOSTON • SYDNEY • AUCKLAND

<u>Notes to Parents</u>

Science is all around you: this series of books encourages children to look around and observe how things work in the pattern of normal life. Each page offers an activity that can be carried out from the illustration with a minimum of equipment. To children, each one is fun to do and to share; for parents there is the reassuring knowledge that the activities are worthwhile and reinforce the children's work at school.

In order to help your children:

* talk through the activities and listen well to their responses

* encourage them to talk about the pictures as much as the science involved

* talk about different approaches to each question, rather than imposing one method of working

* praise them frequently

* don't do too much in one session, but let children return to the pages they enjoy most

Notes on the educational purpose of each topic are listed below, with a reference in brackets to the specific subject area covered.

1   Animal movement
(The variety of life)
Animals move in a variety of ways. The way they move has been formed by the environment in which they live and the way they get their food.

3   Snails and slugs
(The variety of life)
Slugs and snails are gastropods, a name which indicates that they crawl about on their bellies. Both slugs and snails have a muscular foot along which ripples of movement pass as the foot is lifted and brought forward. They lubricate their foot with mucus or slime, which also helps prevent them from drying out.

2   Woodlice
(The variety of life)
Woodlice are common in dark and damp places. They are crustaceans and, having 14 legs, are not insects. They should be kept moist or they will suffocate, since they absorb air through dampness on their bodies.

4   Floating and sinking
(Forces)
Things that are lighter than an equal volume of water will float. When objects that float are held under water you will feel the water pushing them up. Many of the improvised boats will capsize before they are fully laden. This will challenge children to load their boats as evenly as possible.

5 Ramps
(Forces)
If the floor surface is smooth there will be relatively little friction and the car will run far and quickly. You can get the children to measure the distance the car travels in book lengths or ruler lengths. Many children will be content with testing one car against another to decide on the best surface.

6 Moving toys
(Forces)
Your children may have some of the toys shown. Get them to try to explain how they think their toys work. The boats in the paddling pool can be made from polystyrene containers with the mast held in place with modelling clay. The sails can be made from stiff paper.

7 Papers
(Types and uses of materials)
Paper comes in many different grades. If you do the sorting activities, restrict the number of samples. Display the samples by sticking them on the back of a large sheet of old wallpaper.

8 Dissolving
(Types and uses of materials)
This is about powders dissolving. When doing this activity at home, use only a small amount of a few simple substances like flour, sugar, salt and baking powder. When a substance dissolves, it has mixed with the water in pieces too tiny to see.

9 Dissolving and evaporating
(Types and uses of materials)
In the experiment the child is dissolving three or four teaspoons of salt in warm water. Stirring helps the salt to dissolve. Some of the solution is poured into a saucer and the water allowed to evaporate. The salt crystals are left behind, and if you look closely you will see that they are cube-shaped. The experiment could also be done with alum, which you can get from the chemist. Naturally the activity should be supervised, and only water from the tap should be used.

10 Drying up
(Earth and atmosphere)
Water will evaporate especially quickly from both clothes and the ground if the temperature is high and there is good air movement. The puddle is rapidly drying up, as can be seen by the marks chalked around its outline. The water in the wide containers will evaporate more quickly than that in the narrow bottle as there is greater surface area of water.

11 Moving shadows
(The Earth in space)
In summer the sun gets higher in the sky than it does in winter. Notice the bare trees in the winter picture. The shadow of the sundial bottle can be drawn on a sheet of wallpaper. This experiment works well on a windowsill using a pencil stuck vertically in Plasticine. The shadow can be drawn on a smaller piece of paper. Watch the shadow immediately after doing one of the shadow clock outlines. You will see it move.

12 Electricity at home
(Electricity and magnetism)
These pages distinguish between mains electricity and battery power. Standard batteries are almost completely safe for children of this age. **REMEMBER: mains electricity can kill. Children must be warned about the danger.**

13 Transparent things
(Using light)
Light can pass through transparent things but cannot pass through things which are opaque. Water distorts objects seen through it. Light is bent (refracted) as it passes through water. The single drop of water on a thin plastic film acts as a surprisingly strong magnifier.

14 Sound
(Sound and music)
Sound travels more effectively through solids than it does through air. The string of the telephone vibrates, and if you touch it lightly you can feel the vibrations. If you hold it too firmly the vibrations are stopped and the sound is not transmitted. The bottles on the right-hand page can be struck or you can blow across their tops.

1 Animal movement

How do you think these animals move?
Here are some words you might use:
walk, run, hop, slide, swim, fly, swing.

Which animals move quickly?
Which move slowly?
Which animals move in several different ways?

2 Woodlice

You can find woodlice under stones or pieces of wood.
Where do you think they will go when it's hot?

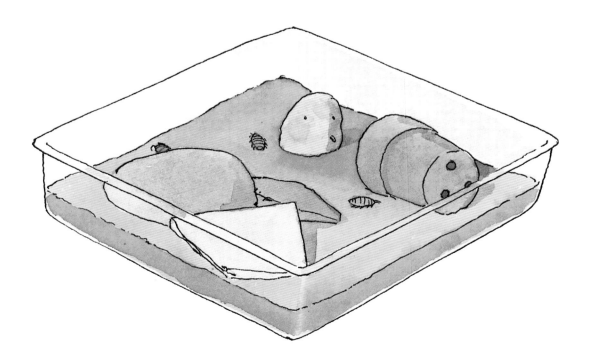

You could keep woodlice in a box like this for a few days. But always put living things back where they belong.

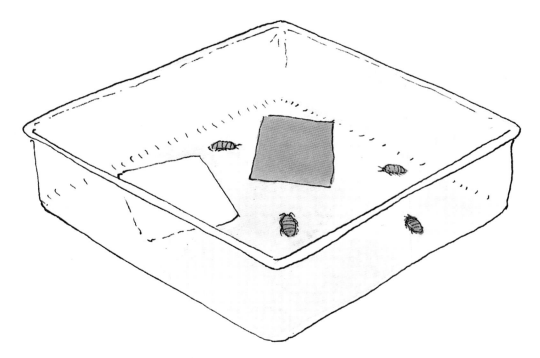

The pink paper is damp. The white paper is dry. Where do you think the woodlice will go?

3 Snails and slugs

Slugs and snails have eyes on stalks.
They also have feelers.
What do you think the feelers are used for?

Put a slug or snail in a glass jar with some damp
soil or paper.
Watch through the glass as the animal glides
along on its foot.
What can you see?

4 Floating and sinking

Which of these things do you
think will float?
Which do you think will sink?
Try some of them and see.

All these things will make good boats to play with.
Which do you think will carry most weight?
Which will go soggy most quickly?

5 Ramps

How could you find out which of your cars goes furthest?
How could you make the test fair for each car?
In this picture you can see hard floors, carpet and
a thick rug. On which of these surfaces do you think the
cars would run best?

6 Moving toys

What do you think makes each of these toys move?
It could be: children pushing, clockwork, rubber
band, children blowing, batteries, springs.

7 Papers

Here is a collection of papers.
Can you recognize newspaper, shiny magazine paper,
kitchen paper, cardboard, tissue, writing paper,
sandpaper and greaseproof paper?
What is each one used for around your house?

tissue

newspaper

shiny magazine

greaseproof

Which do you think is the hardest of the four papers?
Which is the easiest to write on?
Which is the easiest to tear?

tissue

newspaper

shiny magazine

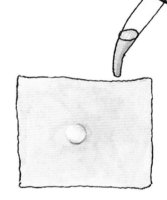
greaseproof

Drops of water were put on these papers.
Which one do you think soaked up water most easily?

8 Dissolving

Which of these do you think will dissolve in
warm water from the tap?

Use one spoon to stir. Keep the others dry to spoon out tiny amounts of each.

salt

sugar

flour

cocoa

Which of these would you say has dissolved completely? You could try these tests yourself.

9 Dissolving and evaporating

You need salt and a spoon.

Fill a jug with water.

Pour out a spoonful of salt.

Stir the salt into the jug.

This boy is making salt crystals.
Describe what he is doing in each picture.